THE MYSTERIOUS CASE
OF
THE SINKING FLA

Written by Cath Hassell & Illustrated by Jon Evans

It was raining in the zoo.

A lot.

In fact it was pouring.

But Frankie the flamingo didn't mind. She puffed up her feathers to stay nice and snug and hummed a little tune.

But then she began to notice something odd. Her leg was getting wetter and wetter!

Frankie was puzzled. Could that be right?

Was the water level rising?

Or ....
     was she sinking?
          Into the mud?

It was all very mysterious and something needed to be done. But the other flamingos hadn't even noticed anything was different!

"I shall have to investigate," said Frankie determinedly as she sploshed off.

At first everything seemed just as it always did. And then she spotted something different...

a pipe...

...with water gushing out of it!

The pipe was coming from the aquarium.

"Are the fish trying to escape?

How exciting!"

Frankie looked up.

It was rain filling up the pool!
How clever is that?

Frankie felt a bit smug.

"Great! I've solved
the mystery!"

The water was coming down a pipe from the roof.

"But if it keeps on raining the water might wash away the nests by the pool".

"Oh Nooooooooo!!!"

"I will have to carry on investigating!" Frankie declared as she sploshed off again.

Ah ha! Another pipe! Frankie stared at it for a long, long time. Surely a real investigator would go down the pipe to find out where it went.

But the pipe looked a bit small for a flamingo.

Frankie ummed and ahhed. Maybe she should come back another day.

Suddenly a furry face appeared.

SpLOSH!

"Rhodri!" spluttered Frankie as she came up for air.

"What are you doing in there?"

"I live here!" exclaimed Rhodri. "There are loads of underground pipes called drains and sewers. Rain that falls on roofs and roads, and waste water from loos and baths and showers and sinks all gets mixed up together and travels for miles and miles underground. It is very, very cool!"

Frankie looked a bit doubtful. Surely it was all a bit dark... and damp... and smelly...?

"The sewer carries all the dirty water to a sewage treatment plant," continued Rhodri, "where it is cleaned and put into the sea. Only, when it ..."

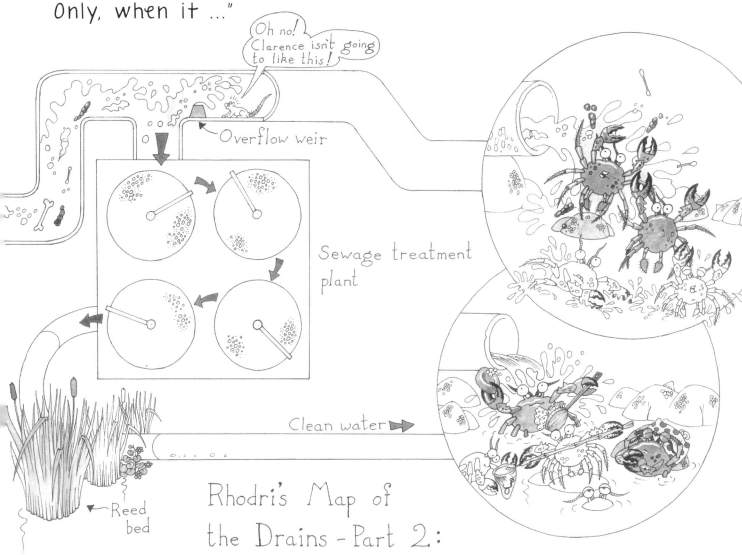

Oh no! Clarence isn't going to like this!

Overflow weir

Sewage treatment plant

Clean water

Reed bed

Rhodri's Map of the Drains - Part 2:

"WOW!" interrupted Frankie. "A SEWAGE TREATMENT PLANT! I must go and see one in action."

Frankie stopped by the river. She was tired and a bit lost. Investigating was harder work than she thought.

Suddenly she heard a mysterious plopping sound and jumped a little.

"Hello Frankie," said Sameera the stickleback. "I've heard that your pool is filled up with rainwater when it rains. Do you know how BRILLIANT that is?"

"It means that less water is taken from our river and so it is easier for us to breathe."

"The flamingo pool is filled from your river!" exclaimed Frankie. "I thought the water comes from a hose!"

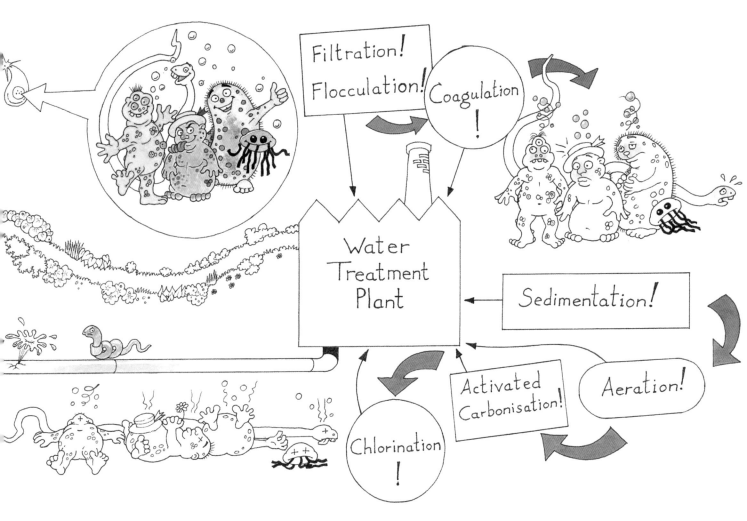

"Well yes that's true Frankie," replied Sameera in her best explaining voice, "but before the water gets to the tap in the zoo, it has been taken from our river, stored in a reservoir, cleaned and pumped to the town."

"Usually there is enough water for everyone. But, if it hasn't rained enough and the people in the town use too much water, the reservoir gets emptier and emptier and more water has to be taken from our river."

"Because we get our oxygen from water and not from the air like you, we need lots of water in our river to be able to breathe properly," continued Sameera, and she pulled out a photograph to show Frankie what she meant.

Frankie couldn't imagine what it must be like to not be able to breathe and suddenly felt a bit faint and had to sit down.

"So you see," continued Sameera, "if everyone used less water, that would never happen to us again!"

Frankie stared at the big pipe and wondered if she was lost. Again.

Suddenly there was a mysterious rustling, scraping sound. Frankie jumped so high she actually hit her head on a seagull!

"Hello Frankie," said Clarence the crab. "I've heard that your pool is filled up with rainwater when it rains. Do you know how BRILLIANT that is? It means that when it rains really hard we are less likely to get poo on our heads."

"Poo on your head," gasped Frankie. "How does that happen?" "Well," said Clarence in his best explaining voice, "when it rains a lot, the sewers get full of water, and there is no space at the sewage treatment plant. So, there is nowhere else for the water to go except out to sea."

"And because the rainwater is mixed with water from the toilets, the poo goes out to sea as well and then, if we are in the way..." and Clarence pulled out a photo to show Frankie what he meant.

Frankie couldn't imagine what it must be like to be covered in poo and suddenly felt a bit faint and had to sit down.

"So you see," continued Clarence, "if everyone collected rainwater from their roof and used it to water their garden if they didn't have a flamingo pool, we would never get poo on our heads again!"

Frankie was back at the zoo. "So I wasn't sinking at all!" she explained to Farah and Freddie. "And the crocodiles weren't escaping into our pool! But it was definitely a mystery, and I solved it! Though Rhodri, Clarence and Sameera all helped."

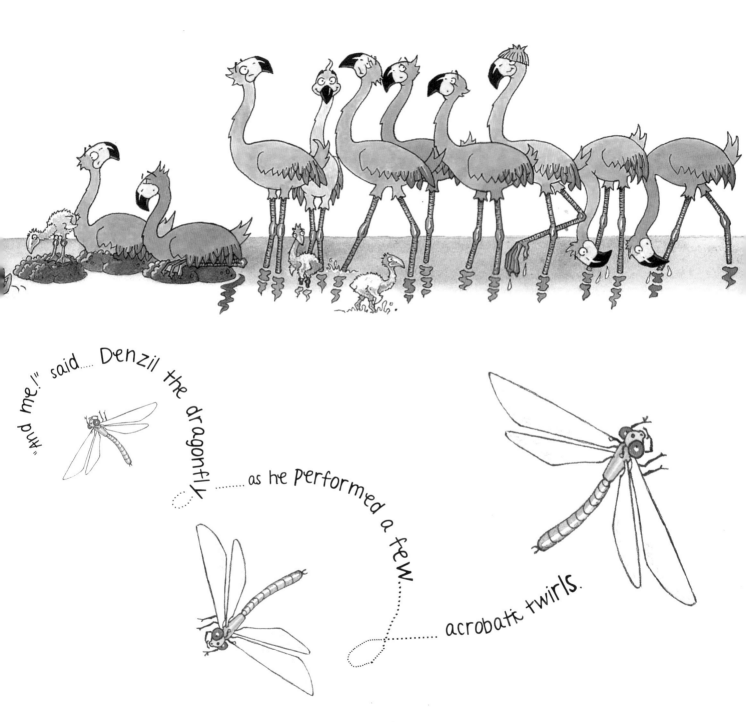

"And me!" said Denzil the dragonfly as he performed a few acrobatic twirls.

Frankie ignored Denzil, as she always did, and continued...

"So, I have set up the Flamingo Investigation Department to make sure that everyone knows what to do so that Sameera and her friends don't run out of water in their river. And that Clarence and his friends don't end up with poo on their heads."

Some important messages from the FID

Water is fun! Enjoy playing in it, and with it, and investigating all about it.

Remember... it's COOL to save water!